Parallel Lines

PARALLEL LINES

CLIONA HENDERSON

Acknowledgements

— • —

I'd like to thank my sister Darragh for encouraging me to write more, or this book would never have happened.

Thanks to my husband, Rob, for his humour and backing.

Thanks to Helen for listening to me, and to Linda and Phil, and Charlotte and Steve, for the Welsh holiday memories.

Contents

— • —

Parallel Lines

— • —

The invisible killer disease that seemed so far away from reality... *no, I'm not going to pick it up!* I clean my trolley religiously at the cleaning station at Tesco every week. I keep my mask loosely on (and stick my tongue out just enough so it's gingerly away from my makeup). I hate that it makes my face sweat and seems to magically wipe half my foundation and lippy onto the mask. What a waste of money!

The usual *Do not fucking cough or breathe on me... keep your distance in the aisles.*

Do you think you're more important, that you can reach over me to get that cheese? I mutter under my breath. I

1

hate Tesco shopping now, with this new normal, as you call it.

Not many people take notice anymore of the one-way system, the two-metre separation.

Do you mind! This is MY personal space.

However, with all these rules in place and my meticulous use of hand sanitizer, I still managed to go to Wales and bring back the coveted trophy of Covid disease.

So, the countdown.

How did I blinking get it?

Retrace my steps, ok.

Now, this is an interesting task, bearing in mind I cannot remember why I go upstairs on a mean mission to get a tape measure; by the time I get to destination B, I'm distracted by the dog's bone on the stair... pick up numerous piles of kids' stuff... you know the piles... wishing that the owner wouldn't just step over them miraculously en route to their destination. I grumble to myself, wondering how I ended up there carrying school books and chargers and odd socks and . . . *So, I'm up here—why?*

You can see how it is. I'm not losing my memory. I'm not going senile. I'm just constantly torn by the accumulation of unresolved mess in this house.

Now that you mention it, it was—yes, the tape measure, as the plumber wants the width of the radiator that I have on order so that he can order the parts.

I think I need to bring you into the picture.

When this Covid-19 thing started, we had just begun demolition works on our lovely family home.

February 2021

— • —

Four months tops... but let's add two months for Contingencies.

We would have started last November—oh, what, a year ago today? But we felt we wanted a family home for Christmas, so pushed it back to spring.

Springtime is perfect. Spring is in the air. The weather is so much better in spring. A good start to the new year, they say.

We can get rid of all the years and years of stuff that we don't need or care for. Stuff that happily finds a home in a space that needs filling. Stuff that scarily

5

accumulates around us and seems to suck the living soul out of any clear space we may have had.

Yes, spring. A good spring clean; a great start to everything.

New Year's resolution! A clean start to skip the crap.

Tear the house down!

Holy moly!

What have we started…?

I feel excited, empowered. The extension we've talked about and saved for for 20 years.

It's beginning.

Yeh, we can do without a kitchen sink, a kitchen, an oven, a dishwasher… we're doing it!

We're doing what we've talked about for years!

Yeh, sure… take it all out.

Sure, it'll only be a few weeks, they say.

Do you need a temporary sink? they ask.

Ah, sure we can cope with the bathroom sink. What's a few dishes?

It's all going to be wonderful.

Wake The Hell Up!

Reality strikes, and we have lost half the house.... The whole back of the house is completely open to the elements. The two kids' bedrooms have had big holes knocked through them to cater for the new flashings of the glass roof. Did I mention my husband is an architect? So yeh, no stress on the details.

The kids' bedrooms are exposed, the kitchen is gone, the garden is now a heap of rubble and we have free access from the garden straight through to the base of the stairwell.

Only saying this as the skip is now the talk of the village. Not only do we get visiting flybys and white vans that help themselves; we also get our lovely neighbours arriving in our house at 8.00 on a Saturday morning.

7

Let me introduce you to delightful Carole at the back.

We are blessed with a neighbourhood watch, i.e., over-60s who have nothing better to do than spy on the square at 2.00 am whilst making a milky brew.

On Saturday mornings, after a long week at work, we look forward to our lie-ins now the kids have grown up.

It's 8.00 am and I'm in the Land of Nod, as usual. I'm one of those creatures who need 40 hours of sleep a week to be able to function through the day.

All we hear is a Gollum-like screech of 'Robbb? Rob, are you there?'

It was like something out of a horror movie, yet it felt real. Too real.

Like within the walls. Like *in* our house.

I jerk out of my sleep and look across at Rob, who, like a synchronised swimmer, leaps out of bed and throws on his dressing gown (his hoody). We don't own dressing gowns.

He peers over the banister, about to reach for a tennis racket, to discover our little old pensioner is standing, clear as day, at the base of our stairs.

'Oh, good morning, Carole,' he says.

'Oh, Rob, I just needed to have a word...'

Our brains are flitting over the possibilities. *Oh no, did the builders do something? Are we too noisy? Have we damaged something?* The list is endless. After all, we are living in a building site.

'Is everything ok?'

'Oh yes, I just need to have a quick word.'

Eight in the morning, mind...

So my gallant, charming husband pops down the stairs to listen to this important piece of information that needs to be communicated at that time of day and can't wait.

9

'Well, Rob, you see, I was having my usual 2.00 am brew and, as one does, having a nosey out the window, and you'll never believe what I saw!'

'No, Carole, what did you see?'

'Well, you know Des, at number 18 on the corner?' she whispers. 'He was throwing a white bag into your skip! Now, you never know what might be in it, and I thought I'd let you know.'

'Ok, thanks, Carole. I'm sure it's fine.'

'Right, so I'm off. Just thought I'd let you know, out of courtesy.'

'No problem, Carole. That's fine.'

'And, oh Rob?' she says. 'Em, I have a large Hoover I don't use anymore. Any chance you could pick it up and dispose of it for me?'

'Yes, Carole, that's no problem…'

Sneaky old bird.

Back to the living quarters.

We are squeezed into the front room, the posh front room that we use for visitors. The secondary living space we once used for a nice toasty fire at Christmas has now become the centre of our universe.

It's the kitchen, the larder, the living room and the temporary sleeping quarters when the sister comes home from Lanza and needs somewhere to rest her head—not that we get any sleep when she visits as we are Irish and we have the world and its wife to sort out.

I'll keep the sister and her antics for a different book—called *I survived Lanzarote*—and go back to *I'm Surviving Covid*.

————— • —————

So where was I…?

Yes, how did I get Covid?

11

I know that we are advised not to travel

I me being me... I am a stickler for the
rules, a⌐ s have been. It must have been the Irish
Catholic upbringing and the guilt. Yes, well, moving
on... That was such a long time ago, and I'm still
clinging on desperately to say I'm Irish, even though
I've lived in the UK for more than three-quarters of
my life. Yes, I still sound Irish and am proud I have
my Irish passport and am still part of the EU, post
Brexit, the word people thought would rule the media
for years until Covid-19 hit us straight in the face.

I can still do Irish dancing very well (if you can
imagine a 48-year-old female with ample tits and a few
pounds too many), especially when I'm asked to do a
party piece in the pub, with a few too many...

Before now, I had the whole village up, teaching
them hop one, two, three, up and hop one, two, three.

There's video evidence these days. Video phones should not have been invented!

And Catholic… well, there's no need for me to get even started on that now, is there?

Anyway, I digress.

The last trip abroad for us was Valentine's weekend 2019, to Budapest, an amazing place. Just before the shit hit the fan or Wuhan, as it's called.

So between the lockdowns, we stayed put. In lockdown, we stayed put. We walked the dogs, walked, worked and slept. We stayed put.

Oblivious to how the world would look in October 2021, we decided to book a wee caravan by the beach in Wales, really to get out of our dusty house/building site for some much-needed R and R.

It was a joint decision with a few family friends in the village.

Let's go away! At the time, I was so excited to get away, the four of us. The idea of a nice family walk along the beach, the fresh air in our lungs, the kids running into the waves, hubby and me holding hands, swinging arms, the sea, the sand... My dream of family bliss was rudely interrupted by:

'I hate the sea! I hate sand!'

'What's the point of going to a caravan in October? I'd rather stay here.'

'I've a football match to go to.'

'I'm visiting my friends on Monday. There's a party...'

Aghhhhhhhhhhhh.

So now you know why we went to Wales: to get away from the constant dust we're breathing in, to have a bit of social engagement and to pretend it was like old times.

We were desperate for the sun. 'Where the sun shines on the righteous' is my husband's favourite phrase when it comes to Wales and his home turf. I beg to differ. I prefer Italy, but that's another story. We were grounded. We were not flying, so Wales it was.

What I forgot to mention were the kids. The kids were of that age when they didn't want to come.

Yes, all our family friends in the village have kids, as we do, but over lockdown, our kids have transformed somewhat from lovely, cute little children who needed us for pretty much everything, from tying their laces to making them breakfast and helping with their homework, to…

Well, with one of them, we have witnessed the evolution into manhood.

My little, smiley, chubby-faced boy has disappeared in a sprawl of long, wild, dark, curly hair, with whispers of facial hair peeping out from under a duvet and a

15

beanie cap, which, to be fair, is only evidenced when the need to relieve himself is irresistible.

The lockdown summer ritual starts about midday when bodily functions force some movement upward from the sleeping position.

The duvet, seemingly now sewn permanently to his very skin, animates magically from a once-sleeping plateau into a whirl of motion, a burst of energetic twists and turns. Completely at one with the entangled duvet is my growing son, now upright and dancing delicately on his tiptoes, proudly releasing bursts of Hamilton prose. His newly found, much deeper, dulcet vocals have swallowed up and replaced my baby boy's young voice.

He whirls to the bathroom, phone in hand. I'm lucky to catch a glimpse from my bedroom as he whizzes past.

He flits across the small stretch of landing from his bedroom door to the bathroom, his sanctuary, his haven, which then encases him for a least an hour. The world outside disappears, even to the frantic knocking on the door from his mother, saying, 'You've been in there an hour. There's a queue!'

Thank goodness we are soon to have bathroom and toilet number two.

For the child, it's the thought of having to spend a week with parents' friends and young kids versus catching up with a year's worth of misspent youth; because of Covid, he gets to stay home with his big sister and the dog.

So, we've booked Friday to Friday.

That's fine. I'm self-employed. I can go when I like. I'm not one of those people who plan for a week, spend another week thinking about what to pack and take a third week to match all the outfits to shoes. No, no, no.

17

I'm more of the type to wing it, chuck it in, and if I forget something, there are always the shops.

So packing and me—a no go, ever since I was a student and would arrive home from Scotland with a little travel bag, 10kg, and in my handbag an extra pair of clean knickers and a can of tuna for emergencies.

My mother still shakes her head to this day.

'Cliona,' she'd say, 'how do you survive?'

I'd say, 'Sure, Mum, it's always an excuse to buy something new.' And I still have my can of tuna.

So this time, we had no worries about the weight of our luggage, no having to stick the suitcase on the scale, a scientific ritual that my husband performs annually to avoid the embarrassment of being overweight at the airport.

It's 19.5kg: you can fit in one more item.

It's 20.25kg: take a flip-flop out.

Now that I'm older and more sophisticated, I've bought him a wee gadget that gives you a much better reading.

So, with no worries about airport luggage restrictions, I don't think very much about packing until it is time to go.

The joiner has been in the house since the crack of dawn, so I have been busy keeping him watered with cups of tea and a chat between answering emails on my phone and tying up loose ends before embarking on a week away from the office/house/building site. *Oh yes, remember to put that 'Out of office' message on.*

Before I go, I had better chase the builder.

The list:

Where are the architraves?

When is the plasterer here?

When is the tiler completing the grouting?

19

We're away for a week, and you have a key. I know everything will be complete by the time we get back!

Working in the construction trade, I should have blinking known better.

The four months have stretched to six months, nine months, and a bit. The joke that we'd be done for Christmas is becoming a lot more real!

I tell ya, if I hear 'Oh, it's delayed because of Covid' one more time... God help me and give me strength.

I understand the delays on the timber. We have passed that stage. I understand that brickies are like gold dust, but when is it going to be done?

It's Friday. Tools down at 3.00—at a push.

So Wales, I'm off. Bye-bye, joiner. It'll be done when we return. (Not a chance in hell.)

I nip to the fridge as I've only had cups of coffee all day.

No, you can't eat or, indeed, cook in my kitchen yet or in front of the builders, and as I'm going away, the kids have been given money for food.

I scan the fridge—my big, fancy, American fridge, may I add?

Don't really fancy an unappetising wet piece of lettuce, don't have time to make anything like a healthy salad, mind, so I grab an Actimel (good for cholesterol) and a Babybel, half-fat, of course, and I'm off. Can get a food shop when I'm there.

Chuck a suitcase in the boot, seatbelt on, down the Actimel, followed shortly by the Babybel. Now that I'm fed, as if in unison, the red light flashes: I need diesel, for the beast, of course.

I'll stop for some rations, too. As this is about a three-hour journey on a Friday, when half the nation heads to join the tunnel neck into God's country, I will need rations. And where the heck am I going?

21

The usual trip to Bennlech I can do with my eyes closed, but with this being a deviation from the norm, I'd better phone my friend to check the postcode.

'I'm on my way. So where are we going?' I add.

Thankfully, my friend is already there, and I type in the digits. 'Right, I'm on my way. Be there by 7.00!'

Tunes blaring, postcode in, I'm on my holiday. Whoop!

I sing along with the songs as if I'm the next winner on The X Factor. I sang solo as a kid, you know. Yes, little me singing solo in the church choir! I stood at the altar in my blue suit and red tights—holy God. I'm not sure what my mother was thinking—and my bowl haircut. If you want to give your child a complex…

I had such an angelic voice when I was young, knew every word to every hymn, but then, again, I was going to be a nun, wasn't I? The brainwashing teachings of the Catholic organisations—feed the orphans, ban

22

apartheid—it's your calling. Fuck me, I was thinking about it: brainwashed into going to feed the kids of Africa to keep my soul white.

And then I grew up and met boys.

Speaking of which... I'm now going to Wales on my own. So much for plans. As my dad used to say, what's the point of making plans? They are there to be changed. I suppose we had to have something to look forward to when we made these plans in March when we were stuck indoors and were restricted to within our own border-lines. I now know where our border starts and finishes, and didn't you know it if someone from the next village came to drink in one of our pubs! It was like witchery; damn that person who lives exactly one millimetre south of the borderline! He might be contagious.

Escape to Wales

— • —

I have a three-berth caravan rented out for me. Cailbhe and Sam stay at home; hubby has a football match to attend. He says, 'Ah, sure, I'll come and join you Sunday. I'll see my mum for lunch and catch you at teatime.'

Ok, it's a blinking bank holiday, so I'm going on my own. I've paid for it, it's too late to get my money back and I need to get out of the village. It's not often I get to be on my own these days, so I thought, 'Ok, I'll head and see you there.'

At least I can leave the dog behind. She needs 100% attention as she's able to disappear in the blink of an eye when we're anywhere near a beach. That's another story when I lost her for half an hour at Red Wharf Bay while she chased seagulls. I'm surprised we got her back, but the heavens opened and she came running back. Beach equals lead from now on.

So, no shopping till tomorrow, eh? I'll still need to grab some Prosecco or wine if I'm going to be on my own tonight.

I'll make sure, that's a definite, as I don't know what the plans are for later. The first thing I'm going to do after reporting in and getting the keys is to check out the beach.

It's my haven, my breath of fresh air, and since we have been cooped up for the last 18 months, I need this!

I don't care if it's cold or breezy or that I am on my own. I'll get my steps in, breathe in the sea air and be happy to be alive.

I am an artist and get inspiration from the sea. The light is magical, and I love how the reflections resonate between sea and air.

I'm in my happy place.

I'm meeting the other two families later. I've already explained that I'm now a party of one rather than a party of four, and having no young kids with me, I don't need to go to the noisy kiddy entertainment that kills your soul. I told them I'd meet them later for a few drinks.

So, I'm in my caravan, and it's so quiet. I check in with the family and report I've arrived without any major drama and found the location easily enough. The family are used to my dramas and the fact I don't know my left from my right. If it wasn't for the scouts I was in in my younger days, I'd end up on an adventure to the other side of the country. The attendants at the entrance weren't too helpful, so I had to navigate with my expert scouting skills, driving whilst reading a map in the dark.

I've unpacked my suitcase and throw myself starfish on the bed. I have a double bed all to myself.

It's a nice location, on a corner plot and a stone's throw from the sea.

Tonight's entertainment: meet at the central hut at 7.00. Well, that gives me time for a shower and that's it.

It's casual attire—jeans and a top, plus the essential face mask. I now have some masks to match my outfits—in the car, in the handbag, in the boot; take your pick.

It didn't take much: black on black, always a good colour to wear; takes pounds off ya. And there's no thinking involved—always helpful when you've lots to juggle. (So much for that Colour Me Beautiful gift my hubby bought me years ago, the therapist trying to include colour in my wardrobe. Eh, no.)

28

Having completed well over my 10,000 steps (very proud of myself, and I really would be a supermodel if I lived by the beach), I can partake in a few well-earned drinks, I naively think to myself as I meander up to the entertainment centre. A nice glass of bubbly and quiet chit-chat into the evening, with not a care in the world. I was most rudely disillusioned.

No wonder my family didn't want to come.

Blow me over! Getting away from my village just to meet half the village here!

Oh hallo, oh hallo, oh hallo! Jesus Christ, this was going to be my place of serenity and peace. I go further into the deluge of noise, the pings and pongs of machines, the loud screaming children and decking loud entertainment. I couldn't blinking hear myself, never mind the chit-chat.

Then the queues to get in ... Another reason my family stayed well clear; every other body on the planet has decided to get away for the weekend to the same venue. We've all been cramped up at home for twelve months, and we all had the same idea. Light bulb moment, not!

I go to the bar and what seems like an hour later order a large bottle of Prosecco. These need to keep coming if I'm going to stay here for more than 10 minutes.

I finally get to sit down, and the children's entertainment ends, thank God. What I don't get is why the hell the speakers have to be blaring so loudly even the dead can hear it.

Seriously, my questioning whether I'm going slightly deaf or choosing to hear only when I need to hear has been answered. I can definitely hear a mouse squeak after this.

My friends, who arrived at 2.00 pm, have partaken in a significant amount more than me. (I understand why now.) They're already going onto the dance floor to dance to Queen. Having only recently arrived, I am completely sober so am happy watching from the sidelines for a moment.

Next thing, Linda was up on the stage, and we stood up from our chairs and were dancing side by side, matching her movements.

As she banged her fists together and then thrust them towards us, we repeated it back, yes, all of us in a row.

We thought we were great and carried on this new routine in unison till the end of the song. Check us cool kids out. Little did we know what we were doing. When she came back to us from the stage, laughing her head off, she explained that we were telling each other 'fuck you', as demonstrated by Ross in *Friends*.

Well, that was it. That gesture was there to stay for the entire weekend.

I relaxed after that and was up dancing for the rest of the night. We ended up dancing with our chairs on, i.e., dancing in our circle with our chairs stuck to us. We had gathered that if we moved, our chairs vanished as it was that packed, so we coined a new move called 'chair dancing'. We must have looked like right eejits, but who cares after a few bottles of Prosecco.

It was strange going back to my caravan at the end of the night. All the families bid their farewells, and I walked back alone in the dark with my iPhone light leading the way.

I carried on to the sea and sat there for a while, listening to the ebb and flow of the waves and watching the blue moon glisten on the water. What a lovely end to the day!

I got back to the caravan, weirdly quiet. I charged my phone and assumed my starfish position for the night. Tomorrow, I thought, I will go get some food and art provisions and get some painting done.

Saturday morning

— • —

I'm up and alive at the crack of dawn.

No, I didn't find a wee woman called Dawn in my bed. Sure, I would have had to lose my starfish for that, and besides, I'm not really into women in that way, thanks.

The iPhone pings and it's my hubby, saying he's up as well. He has walked the dog, done the washing and is off to his football match.

He's a lifelong suffering Everton supporter and wouldn't miss a match for the world. I have now become a lifelong wife supporting the Everton sufferer—I mean supporter—and actually, now that I understand the rules of the game, quite enjoy going.

I remember the very first match he took me to against Newcastle Utd. Dear God in heaven.

I remember to this day what I was wearing and what phone I had. Yes, mobiles had just been invented, and I had a tiny blue Alcatel with a sliding top, which fitted neatly into my denim jacket's top right pocket. My hubby thought it would be good to introduce me to the game as we were engaged at the time and he wanted to get me accustomed to the cause.

He took me to the most hideous pub in living memory, with a makeshift toilet for women. Seriously, Liverpool needs to sort this shit out. It was called the Winslow. (Now anyone from Manchester would think 'Ooh, Wilmslow' where the houses start at half a million, so I expected a really nice pub.) Well, I was fooled alright.

I felt like a squashed sardine gasping for oxygen whilst I juggled for an upright position with both feet touching the floor, amongst a rowdy gathering of footie fans from *both* teams. I have had my share of scary moments living in the troubles in Northern Ireland, but this is up there with them. I held my phone and purse tightly whilst linking into his arm as we wrestled to drink a half-pint at the bar. The singing and shouting and the banging and the clapping got louder and louder as the Newcastle fans jumped on the tables, belting out their football anthem, with the Evertonians giving them back as good as they got.

THIS is normal behaviour. Well, I have lived a sheltered life.

I thought a fight was about to erupt, so I threw the half-pint down my neck as fast as you could say 'Jimmy' and asked to leave with my face as you couldn't hear yourself think, never mind speak. My hubby looked at me for a second, laughed at the fact that my pint was gone and my eyes were the size of saucers (now this is a feat when my little slanty eyes do not open very wide) and ushered me out the door.

'Not your kind of pub, love?'

'Er, no!'

I digress. So back to sunny Wales, 'where the sun shines on the righteous' engrained in my brain, having married a Welsh man.

I make myself a coffee, no milk, and head to the shop to get my rations in. Weird buying for one. The shop sells wine, beer, Prosecco, bacon, tuna and salad—and barista milk.

I don't think I'll be doing much cooking, and I think once hubby arrives, we can drink the alcohol or bring it home, if need be ;-)

I find a cute little art shop, which has a weird little entry system, thanks to Covid. They have developed a one-on-one system consisting of a bright red chunky rope across the front door, with a little note saying 'Someone will be with you soon.' I don't have to wait long before a very arty lady with wispy grey hair held back by a bandana greets me at the counter. She's so nice and helpful, and seeing as I've bought so much, she gives me student discount. I'll take that! I feel a sense of accomplishment getting back to the caravan by 11.00.

My friends are going to the zip wires today, so I have a bit of peace to get on with some painting. I got lots of inspiration from my long walk along the sea, so I put some music on and let my creative juices do their work.

A few hours fly by and I create a soft landscape of merging aqua and blues, with fluffy white clouds transposing between sea and land. I haven't painted in a while, and when I do, I wonder why I don't do it more often.

I will buy a house in Italy one day and retire there to paint lovely landscapes of Italian villages carved into spiralling mountains.

Then I remember that back home we have a building site and my once studio is now an office for two—the victim of lockdown and virus and mid-pandemic.

May is the best time to paint outside when the light is right. It's now Halloween when there's no light past 4.00 pm, and I transport myself back to reality.

It's three o'clock! Goodness me, I said I'd meet my friends at 4.00. Right, wash the paint off everything. I haven't mentioned I'm a messy painter and when I'm in the flow, the paint attaches itself not only to the canvas but to my lips, my face, my arms, my fingernails, my arse. Luckily, I have sugar and washing liquid, the best remedy for removing paint from any area of skin. And the arse of my jeans I can clean with a baby wipe. Right, into the shower and get myself ready.

The attire is casual. We're meeting for food.

The pain is because we're still in the pandemic. We are in the stage of 'Eat out to help out' and get '50% Off' sometimes. Now, in order to be served, we have to book to eat anywhere, so if the place is fully booked and we don't get to eat straight away, we'll have a choice of only fish and chips or pizza later.

The fish and chip shop was struggling for deliveries. Yet another result of the pandemic. You could literally get *just* chips, not even a chip butty.

The pizza bar... We had to scan a bar code, wait an age for the Wi-Fi to connect, then download an app, then order, then pay, and the blinking buffer circle would show its head once more, so it wasn't worth the time or effort for a blinking slice of pizza!

41

I wasn't really bothered where I ate, but it was nice to see the guys with the kids in an environment where we could converse without hearing aids.

I put on my nice new white Superdry top and a pair of jeans and went up to meet them. I chose a BBQ chicken wrap and salad.

Whilst I sat there not having to help the children choose their meals, I thought *Isn't it funny watching people order?*

You know what I mean. The food envy of 'Oh, I wish I'd chosen that.' Sometimes it's safer for us all to have the same thing.

What are you having? What are you having?

I should have known better than to choose a BBQ sauce wrap when wearing a white top. Sod's blinking law. I'm worse than a baby. Two seconds and boom! It missed my mouth. I must admit, I do talk a lot, but God has blessed me with a medium-sized mouth but ample boobs that caught the godforsaken, misaligned food parcel.

I looked down and it had landed right slap bang in the middle of my white hoody, this bright orange stain. Ffs, I had no other hoody, and it was obvious that I'd have to go home and get changed. No amount of baby wipes would get this mama of a stain out. (I read that on Instagram once: baby wipes are the cure for most stains.) Another justification for wearing black.

Well, at least I was getting extra steps in.

I paid for my food, washed it down with a cheeky Prosecco, and arranged to meet the guys later. I chose another outfit and caught them back at the entertainment lounge.

It was Saturday night and there was a Halloween special on. *Hmm...*

The night went surprisingly well, and the tribute to Meatloaf was pretty good. The atmosphere was not bad, with plenty of audience participation with magicians and the like.

Meatloaf brings back fond memories of hubby and me driving down the Amalfi Coast on our honeymoon—what a holiday and what a wedding. It was like the wedding feast in the village of Cana; we turned our little Italian village, Barga, into a wedding feast for a week and literally drank them out of alcohol. All we needed was the first miracle to replicate itself and turn the water into wine.

That's what happens when 70 people from England, Ireland, Scotland and Wales get together for a celebration. Biased I am, but it still was the best wedding ever! We even had a fish and chip festival. Right, stop.

Back to Wales.

The Sweeneys, the Parrys and the Leonards were pretty tired after a full day, so we retreated to bed just after 10.00. That's so early for a Saturday night.

44

They went one way and I went another.

I bumped into one of the kids from my village on his own. He's a few years younger than my son, so about 12, and I suggested I walked him home. To be fair, he'd been coming here for years so knew his way home in his sleep, but I felt it was my duty, being a parent and all, and I'd get to see my friend, whom I hadn't seen in a while.

I walked past my caravan and pointed it out, and after another few minutes' walk, we were at their door.

I knocked and said, 'Well, fancy meeting you here! Look who I found!'

I was greeted and warmly welcomed in to a full-on sausage sizzle and a bottle of beer. Those guys knew how to do it.

It was time to allow Chico, their energetic springer spaniel, to let off some steam, so Laura and I left the manor of food and headed to the dunes for a nice, brisk walk. Little did I know that my friend knew the dunes like the back of her hand and the brisk walk was a bit brisker than expected. She seemed to float over the spiky, prickly, dagger-edged, sword-like grasses and got up to the top of the highest dune in seconds, while I seemed to step in the same spot of sand over and over to gain 2 inches in altitude. I finally got to where she was (breathless and feeling like a fat pin cushion), to the summit of all summits, to sit on a sandy mound and let the dog run wild.

We chatted, she smoked. I can't stand smoke; it's one of the worst things on earth, in my book. She talked about finding a dead baby seal earlier in the day, and I was just so glad I hadn't happened to step on it on our midnight walk or, indeed, breathe in the stench of rotting seal. Yuck.

I trusted she knew where we were going. I followed blindly. She glided, I rolled. She jumped, I rolled. She stopped, I rolled right into the middle of a stream, an estuary, a blinking deep, wet sand pit. Thank God she was there because I don't think I would have known my way home, never mind how to get out of the quicksand. To be perfectly honest, I wouldn't have gone gallivanting across the dunes on my own—or would I? She thought it was very funny. I didn't. Another item of clothing for washing.

A Welsh lunch

— • —

Sunday... painting done ✔   Well, a bit of titi-vating and I'd be happy with it. We had a trip planned that day to check out a village nearby, get out for the day, have a change of scenery. I was looking forward to it. The trains weren't running, so we had to drive. As I was only one person, I jumped in with the Sweeneys in their immaculate 4x 4, and we headed to the closest village.

We found a little amusement park open. To be honest, it was daylight robbery for what you got.

This get-up must easily have been going since the 70s and was in desperate need of a spruce-up. The paint on the equipment had faded into rusty reds and yellows. I didn't want to touch anything for fear of rust marks on my clothes and walked gingerly around, trying not to catch anyone's eye. £20 went in the blink of an eye, so we decided to try and grab some lunch.

It was shit. *No one* in Wales would accept a group of six or more into *their* pub, especially during a pandemic. *We should have booked!*

- No one in Wales accepts English people if a Welshy is not with them.
- No one in Wales is friendly towards the Brits if a Celt is not with them.
- No one in Wales likes tourists, especially the English.
- No one in Wales likes children, especially English children.

Cliona to the rescue, *dah dah*!

Next thing: 'Cliona? Eh, you know the way. You're Irish.'

We had already tried every inn in the village, and no one would let us in. I can imagine the 'Mary, Joseph and the little donkey' scenario now and how they must have felt, albeit it was a slightly different ordeal.

I eventually managed to persuade a pub to take the 12 of us in, and I was delighted with myself, but by the time I turned around to excitedly wave them all in, the two couples and their children had decided that enough was enough. They'd had enough rejection for one day, and so we resorted to heading back to the campsite for a drink because, of course, they bloody needed it!

The children spied a sweetie shop on their way, so, to keep them happy, they were allowed £1 each. They hungrily filled their paper bags with tooth decay,

51

and we headed home. A pound doesn't go as far as it did in my day. We did have ¼ pence pieces back then, so four Hairy Mollies for a penny. Just to describe a Hairy Molly, for those who don't know: they were hard-boiled, chocolate-flavoured, sugared balls covered in desiccated coconut. Yummy!

Hey, ho. At least I tried to get lunch, but we agreed it was a shit decision to leave the campsite in the first place. The solution to everything: let's drink!

We had the same entertainment that night in the same location.

We had worked out there was nicer Prosecco for the same price, so we had a few bottles of that and then called it a night.

— • —

I must admit I was looking forward to my hubby arriving the next day! It was decided, on the fact that my hubby was arriving—drum roll, please—that we'd have a get-together with food back at one of the caravans. We all gathered enough food to feed the 5000 and headed to Charlotte and Steve's, the largest caravan on the site.

It was a lovely evening. Six adults, four kids, perfect. Good food and company, but once all the beers and wine were gone, we headed back to ours.

On the way back, though, typically, I didn't want it to end so soon. I am a night owl. The moon was shining brightly, and the weather was calm and mild. I had the romantic thought of meandering slowly to the beach, holding hands with my hubby, and watching the waves roll in.

It's not something we get to do often, so why not? It's a perfect opportunity! It's midnight and the beach will be empty. It's a two-minute walk, I thought.

So, there we were.

The moon glistened, washing the sea with a beautiful pale hue.

It was like being in a black and white film. The waves crashed in and receded. Oh, I just love that sound. You can't beat it. And it was so, so quiet. We stood silently and watched the water, breathing in the freshness of the cool, salty air.

Next thing, I fancied getting in.

It's always been on my bucket list.

'Night Swimming' by Rem started belting through my brain.

I found myself stripping, yes, stripping off. Coat flew to the ground, followed closely by my boots.

Before I knew it, my bra and knickers were thrown on top of my jumper and jeans. I chucked my socks into each boot. Somehow, I managed that in the dark. Then I was mindlessly running, careless and free, stark blinking naked, shouting, 'Come on, I dare you!' into the decking freezing water.

Obviously, the alcohol had started having an effect on me as the cool air didn't bother me.

I was running knee-deep now, gasping as the cold hit my nether regions. 'Come on in,' I shouted. 'It's fabulous!'

But my hubby is a lot more sensible than me—sometimes.

At this moment, I was in my element, thinking *Yes! I'm doing it. I'm actually skinny dipping!*

I also thought one of two scenarios was about to happen: either he was standing at the edge of the water fully clothed and avoiding getting his shoes wet, videoing me being a class one eejit, or...

Next thing, I screamed as the sea water splashed me from all angles and a large force of nature bulldozed past me, screaming, 'Loser!'

All I could see was a pair of pert white bum cheeks disappearing in front of me as he dived into the sea.

I laughed. *He's just confirmed he is as nuts as me, perhaps even more nuts. I'm not getting my hair wet, though. That wouldn't be ideal. Oh, wait… he's under the water and nowhere to be seen.*

I turned around to see if I could spot him. He's a good underwater swimmer. I've learned that on holiday when he can swim from one end of the pool to the other without taking a breath.

Oh shit. Where is he?

I start to panic as he is very unpredictable. He could be lurking underneath, just waiting to—before I know it, my legs are taken from underneath me and I'm going backwards into the sea. I gulp in the cold seawater, realise I have got my head wet, and all of a sudden, I'm blinking freezing.

We then gaze at each other and fall around laughing. Ooh, he is sexy when he is wet.

I love the thing he does when he surfaces from the water, shaking his head and flicking his hair back. He does it every time. Ooh, he is sexy.

We giggle a bit more, splash each other more and then fall into a romantic embrace. I forget where I am and am consumed by him. He picks me up and we are completely absorbed in the moment. I've missed him and he's missed me. I taste the salt on his lips and he's mine.

We cool down rapidly after our passionate tangle and realise we are freezing and a bit reckless.

Ok, let's get out. It's cold, but I'm glad we have done it. It was pretty exhilarating. One for the memory bank. Ok, let's get our clothes.

Our clothes?

Where are they? Oh, no!

With the tide constantly moving and us messing about in the sea, we have moved north of our entry point. When we navigated the waves on the way in, we didn't exactly walk a straight line and had no marker on the land.

Jesus, it's dark. Where are our phones? Where are our clothes? Surely there's no one else on the beach?

We walk up and down the beach a few times, teeth clattering, and finally find a mound. I must say, my two white headlamps are not helping right now!

Oh yes! There they are; they're mine!

I scramble through the pile, take out my phone and turn on the light. Rob, where the heck are yours?

It takes him a minute to spot his pile, and we throw on our hoodies. There's no point in putting on cold, wet jeans, so let's just carry them. We head to the dunes.

I love the sea, but wet sand—ooh, it's just everywhere! What a night!

Rob then remembers his glasses. Oh shit, where are his glasses? Bugger, he cannot do anything without his glasses.

We start combing the beach, up and down, looking for his glasses. This is a challenge in the circumstances. Dark, cold and half-dressed.

We have moved our mounds of clothes, which would have indicated where to start the search. This is a different scenario to the usual sense of beachcombing.

We both have our phone lights on. Thank God for phones—I'll say this only once. I wish mobiles hadn't been invented for common use as the human race becomes addicted to their blue hue.

We scour the tidal lines, praying for them to be found. If we leave it overnight, there will be no chance of finding them. They will either be washed out to sea or buried in the sand for ever.

Rob starts focusing on one area as I watch and stay with the rest of the clothes and shoes, becoming a marker in the sand. If the two of us constantly walked up and down, we would lose our way home, too!

He walks left a few feet, then right a few feet, moving further and further up the shore. I watch with bated breath, wondering what, exactly, he is doing. Next thing, he crouches down and shouts, 'Hurrah!'

No way! He has actually found them. He explains some navy method for finding things, which goes over my head, but at least, thanks be to God, he has them, or he wouldn't have been able to drive his car home!

Well, that's sobered us up! We head home with our wet bodies and clothes and get into the warm shower.

Next morning, we go outside and see a trail of wet socks on the caravan steps. Hahahaha. I went to bed with wet hair, so I spend the next hour untangling it and straightening it into shape.

It's a cold and wet day, but we don't want to stay in the caravan. It's Tuesday, so let's go exploring. We rinsed out our wet clothes, hung them to dry and cleaned the sand from the caravan.

I don't think we will be heading back to the beach for a while.

— • —

Rob made us a lovely breakfast, and once we had cleared up, we were ready to explore.

We ended up in a gorgeous pub in Beddgelert. Gelert is a legendary wolfhound associated with the village of Beddgelert (whose name means 'Gelert's Grave') in Gwynedd, north-west Wales.

In the legend, Llywelyn the Great returns from hunting to find his baby missing, the cradle overturned, and Gelert with a blood-smeared mouth. Llywelyn was

61

convinced that his favourite hound had killed his son. Mad with grief, he took his sword and plunged it into Gelert's heart. As the dog howled in his death agony, Llywelyn heard a child's cry coming from underneath the upturned cradle. It was his son, unharmed!

It's a sad story, and we went looking for the grave, which is situated in the centre of the village. I was surprised at how many people were wandering the streets on such a cold day, but it was nice to be out and about.

We then headed for a walk along the coastline a few villages north and took some gorgeous photos of the waves crashing in against the shore.

Wales is a beautiful place. As we wandered through the village streets, we saw an old cottage. Being in the construction industry, we are always looking at old buildings and their endless possibilities.

This one was a two-storey building set back off the main road and had a number of colourful shells built into the path in a mosaic pattern leading to the entrance. I was busy trying to decipher the message in the text while Rob was looking through the windows. Suddenly, he shouted, 'Oh, Cliona, did you see that?'

I had forgotten that it was Halloween. The owners had decorated the house in true Halloween fashion, with old puppets and paraphernalia hanging from the windows. Very effective, I tell you. With Rob being one for pranking, I should have known better. He got me proper!

I looked up right at the moment the dark shadow moved into the window. It must have been an old theatre or something. The black-clothed mannequin had moving parts, and as its head turned toward me … Jesus, I was off.

Now, as I was saying, I'm active but not very active, with two heavy bosoms weighing me down. Well, I left them still hanging there as I turned into Mo Farah and catapulted myself down the road, screaming. It wasn't until I got to the end of the road they caught up with me.

Rob was still standing where we had stood, bent over, belly laughing. To this day, he laughs about it; he knows my weaknesses and how to get a reaction.

It all started that day he made me watch Freddy Krueger.

'It's not that bad,' he said. 'It's outdated,' he said as the two of us sat side by side on a small sofa in Dublin in the smallest house in the world.

He'll never forget how he turned round to face me at the end with a scary face in the dark, and the imprint I left on his face as my hand automatically reacted. It still shocks me how scared I was and how one can react in the heat of the moment.

It's like when I crashed my car. I had a bad back anyway, but with pure adrenaline, I picked up my baby and marched up a very steep hill, which I wouldn't have been able to do normally. It's either fight or flight!

Coming back to Criccieth, we decided to walk an alternative route back to the car so I wouldn't have to walk past the scary building. Yes, seriously, haunted houses or anything scary like that, and big dogs, for me are a big no-no.

It was getting dark, so we decided to get back and meet the others. Rob hadn't experienced the entertainment yet, and wasn't he in for a surprise.

Honestly, I think it's the last time we'll do this. Our children have grown up, so have no interest, and it really is for the children.

Child number one is 28, so definitely not. She is my mini-me—me in a nutshell, 20 years younger, with a lot more attitude.

Child number two is 16 and a mini Rob. Yes, there's a 12-year gap. After having Cal, I was done. No one tells you about childbirth, do they? It took me 12 years to build up the courage to have another one.

Rob had always wanted a boy to carry on the Henderson name, so I agreed. It was worth it, but never again.

It's weird not having them around. I've enjoyed my little trip, but now I'm ready to go home.

One more night and we're off.

I wonder how they're managing. They get on so well, which is one advantage of the age gap, although sometimes we think Sam is looking after Cal, when it comes to maturity, but that's another story.

I'm glad we had children early. It was tough at the time, but when I see our friends with young ones now, I'm delighted that it's over for me. I should be coming into menopause soon, nearing the big five-o. I wonder when it will start.

Homeward bound

—— • ——

The evening entertainment surpassed our expectations, with a new act of Queen, one of Rob's favourite bands. The acts swap over mid-week so it doesn't get repetitive, so it was actually quite a good evening. As it was our last night, we stayed to the end and danced the night away.

The weather was brutal the next morning, so we made a quick exit and got home before 1.00 pm. The others had a bit more packing to do, so we left them to it.

We looked forward to seeing our brood and went out for a 'welcome home' pub lunch in the village pub.

We're lucky in our village with friends. I missed my mate Helen and her hubby Stephen, who happened to go to Tenerife when we went to Wales, so it was good to catch up with them.

It was a memorable story, how we met. It was my daughter's 17th, actually.

I had flown to Ireland on a break, and Facebook was new.

My hubby had gone to the pub to give her some space while she had a few friends round. Then a lad popped into the pub, asking for our address's location, which raised a few eyebrows.

Next thing, blue lights were flashing, and the same guy appeared, shouting, 'It's all kicking off!'

Stephen, Dave and Rob jumped to the rescue. It turned out the house had been visited by more than a few friends, thanks to Facebook. It also happened to be the night of the Manchester Derby, hence the kick-off. Poor Cal couldn't handle the number of people running through the house, and when the fight broke out, it was unmanageable.

Stephen and Dave, two men built like brick shit houses, are not to be messed with. They entered the house behind Rob, who shouted, 'Right, everyone, whoever should not be here, get the hell out!' in his best Liverpool accent. It's meant to sound tougher or something, and before you knew it, the hooligans were on their merry way and peace was restored to the streets of the village. Heroes!

It was like, 'Ah, we didn't know you lived across the road!' Since then, we have cemented a great friendship with our neighbours and had many a good belly laugh.

— • —

Home, sweet home, although the builders were still there. I think they must have had a holiday, too.

The rules were strict, as you can imagine. We had to do a Covid test before entering the site, and a temperature check was mandatory.

All clear?

But a few weeks after arriving home from Wales, I was still not feeling right. I had gone back to work straight away, as my job could carry on through the pandemic. My symptoms: tired, fatigued, sleepy, lethargic, no concentration... I must have had Covid, surely? Although I hadn't had a cough or fever.

So why am I so tired? Maybe it's the menopause?

The doctors are not open, so everything is online, and it is tricky to get a face-to-face appointment without a long wait.

My hubby says, 'Off to the doc's you go. Just get a check-up,' so I wait for an appointment.

My mind starts to overthink. *You know, I'm nearing 50, so it may be the menopause…* I start Googling the symptoms.

The online doctor responds. 'Could you be pregnant?'

'No, I don't think so.' *Surely not?*

The doc asks, 'Please confirm that you are not pregnant.'

'Are you 100% sure?' Rob asks as we count back the weeks.

'No, I couldn't possibly be, but I'm not sure…'

I had better take a test, then. *Gosh, I haven't a clue where to even buy one, and I'm not going to the local pharmacy.*

I'm only doing this to be sure, I say to myself. *I'm not! It's defo the menopause playing tricks with me, or long Covid…*

'Right, Rob, I have peed on it. You can look first,' I say, wincing.

73

And there you have it, as we stared at each other …

Two *blue* lines on the test stick!

Printed in Great Britain
by Amazon

26994746R00047